Horrid Henry's
Annual 2015

Horrid Henry's Annual 2015

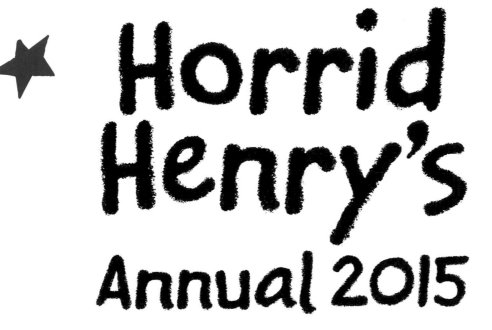

Francesca Simon

Illustrated by Tony Ross

Orion
Children's Books

First published in Great Britain in 2014
by Orion Children's Books
a division of the Orion Publishing Group Ltd
Orion House
5 Upper Saint Martin's Lane
London WC2H 9EA
An Hachette UK Company

1 3 5 7 9 10 8 6 4 2

This compilation, Horrid Henry's Annual 2015 © Orion Children's Books 2014
Design by Envy Design Ltd
Text © Francesca Simon 2014
Illustrations © Tony Ross 2014

Compiled by Sally Byford from the Horrid Henry books
by Francesca Simon & illustrated by Tony Ross

A catalogue record for this book is available from the British Library.

Printed and bound in Germany.

ISBN 978 1 4440 1153 1

www.orionbooks.co.uk
www.horridhenry.co.uk

Contents

Hello Fans

Ahoy, my brave and fearless Purple Hand Gang Members, and welcome to my Annual for 2015!

Phew, what a terrifying year I've had. Well, scary for nappy toad babies, but all in a day's work for an intrepid hero like me. Injection bunnies and wailing graveyard ghosts tried to grab me, and alien acid monsters did their best to scare me to death. HA! And can you believe the Demon Dinner Lady was up to her old tricks? Bah.

Let's go 2015! More thrills, chills, and spills than ever before.

Henry

Spot the Spooks
There are some ghosts hidden throughout this Annual. How many can you find?

Horrid Henry's Nightmare New Year

⭐ Total Sweet Ban.

⭐ Sent to Great-Aunt Greta's for the summer.

⭐ Miss Battle-Axe becomes the new head teacher.

⭐ The TV breaks and Mum and Dad DON'T get a new one.

⭐ Moved to top spelling group.

⭐ Bossy Bill back in my class.

⭐ Perfect Peter on TV.

★ Terminator Gladiator cancelled.

★ Peter comes Trick or Treating with me dressed as a bunny.

★ Christmas with Stuck-Up Steve.

★ Miss Tutu's dance class starts up again.

★ Rabid Rebecca comes to babysit every night.

★ Only computer game I'm allowed to play is *Name that vegetable*.

★ Only TV programme I'm allowed to watch is *Manners with Maggie*.

AAAARRRGGHH! I get shivery just imagining ANY of those horrible things coming true.

13

Horrid Henry's Nightmare Night

Nightmare New Year Quiz

1. It's Horrid Henry's turn to see Nurse Needle for his injection. What does Moody Margaret tell Henry just before he goes in?

   (a) The needle is as long as my leg.
   (b) The needles are so big and sharp they can go right through your arm.
   (c) Don't worry, Henry, Nurse Needle will give you a nice biscuit.

2. How does Horrid Henry make sure that his nightmare cousin, Stuck-up Steve, doesn't get all the best toys at Christmas?

   (a) He throws all of Stuck-up Steve's presents in the dustbin.
   (b) He swaps round the tags so he gets the good presents.
   (c) He hides Stuck-up Steve's presents in his bedroom.

3. Henry is horrified when Moody Margaret moves in for two weeks. What does she do to spoil Henry's bedtime?

   (a) Pinches his cuddly toy, Mr Kill.
   (b) Plays her trumpet very loudly all night.
   (c) Fills his bed with jam, crumbs and something squishy-squashy and horrible.

4. When Henry spends the day at his dad's work, he meets Bossy Bill, the son of Dad's boss. How does Bossy Bill get Henry into trouble?

   (a) By blaming Henry for putting salt in the tea.
   (b) By telling his dad that Henry licked his fingers and dipped them into the sugar bowl.
   (c) By pouring all the sugar down the toilet and blaming Henry.

5. Rabid Rebecca is the most monstrous and nightmarish babysitter ever. What has Henry heard about her?

(a) She let Moody Margaret do a makeover on her and paid her £1.

(b) She made Tough Toby get in his pyjamas at five o'clock and do all his homework.

(c) She laughed at all Rude Ralph's rude jokes.

6. Why does Henry think New Nick's little sister Lisping Lily is a nightmare?

(a) She wants to marry him.

(b) She wants him to play with her.

(c) She wants to kiss Perfect Peter.

7. Why doesn't Horrid Henry like his swimming teacher Soggy Sid?

(a) He doesn't let Henry go in the water.

(b) He tells Henry there's a shark in the pool.

(c) He never listens to any of Henry's excuses and makes him go in the water.

8. Why is Greasy Greta the Demon Dinner Lady such a nightmare?

(a) She snatches all the sweets and treats from the kids' packed lunches.

(b) She snatches the carrots, grapes and healthy snacks from the kids' packed lunches.

(c) She ladles out double portions of soggy semolina.

How did you do? Check your answers on page 74.

Check your answers on page 74.

6-8   Amazing! You know loads about Horrid Henry's evil enemies and why they give him nasty nightmares.

3-5   Not bad! Just read more Horrid Henry books at bedtime and you're sure to get a better score next time.

1-2   AAAAGGGHHH! Your score is a total nightmare!!

Horrid Henry's Nightmare

"MUM!" screamed Peter. "Henry called me baby boo boo."

"Stop being horrid, Henry, and be nice to your brother," shouted Mum. "Or I'll send Ralph home."

"I wasn't being horrid," bellowed Henry. Oh to be a wizard and turn Peter into a toadstool.

"Okay, Peter, you can stay," snarled Henry. "But you'll be sorry."

"No I won't," said Peter.

"We're telling scary stories," said Ralph.

"And you hate scary stories," said Henry.

Peter considered. It was true, he hated being scared. And almost everything scared him. But maybe that was last week. Maybe now that he was a week older he wouldn't be scared any more.

"I'm brave now," said Peter.

Horrid Henry shrugged. "Well, just don't blame me when you wake up screaming tonight," he shrieked.

Peter jumped. Should he stay and listen to these terrible tales? Then he squared his shoulders. He wasn't a baby, whatever Henry said. He was a big boy.

Horrid Henry told his scariest story about the child-eating vampire werewolf. Rude Ralph told his scariest story about the wailing graveyard ghost who slurped up babies. Then Henry told his most scary story ever in the history of the world: the alien acid monster and zombie mummy who –

"I know a scary story," interrupted Peter.

"We don't want to hear it," said Henry.

"It's really scary, I promise," said Peter. "Once upon a time there was a bunny . . ."

"SCARY stories!" shouted Rude Ralph.

"Once upon a time there was a really big bunny," said Peter. "And one day his little tail fell off."

18

Peter paused.

"Is that it?" said Henry.

"Yes," said Peter.

"Blecccchhhh," belched Rude Ralph.

"That's your idea of a scary story?" said Henry. "A bunny with no tail?"

"Wouldn't you be scared if you were a bunny and your tail fell off?" said Peter.

"Isn't it time for you to practise your cello?" said Henry.

Peter gasped.

He didn't ever like to miss a day's practice.

Perfect Peter trotted off.

Phew. Worm-free at last.

"Now, as I was telling you, Ralph," said Horrid Henry, "there was once a zombie mummy that roamed . . ."

NO!!!!!

Horrid Henry lay in bed in his dark bedroom, trembling. What a horrible, horrible nightmare. All about a ghost bunny with huge teeth and no tail, charging at him waving a gigantic needle. Ugggh. His heart was pounding so fast he thought it would pop out of his chest.

But what to do, what to do?

Henry was too scared to stay in bed. Henry was too scared to move. Don't be an idiot, snarled Devil 1. There is no such thing as a ghost bunny. Yeah, you lummox, snarled Devil 2. What a wimp. Frankly, I'm disappointed.

But Horrid Henry was too terrified to listen to reason. What if that alien acid monster or the ghost bunny was hiding under his bed? Horrid Henry wanted to lean over and check, but he couldn't. Because what if the wailing graveyard ghost had sneaked into his wardrobe and was just waiting to GRAB him?

Is Horrid Henry brave enough to get out of bed and look in the wardrobe? Find out in **'Horrid Henry's Nightmare'** from *Horrid Henry's Nightmare.*

Worst Nightmares and Secret Dreams

Perfect Peter

WORST NIGHTMARE
Eating chips, burgers and pizza every day, with NO fresh fruit or vegetables.

SECRET DREAM
Marrying Miss Lovely.

Miss Battle-Axe

WORST NIGHTMARE
Teaching Horrid Henry and Rude Ralph FOR EVER.

SECRET DREAM
Winning a season ticket to watch her favourite football team.

Moody Margaret

WORST NIGHTMARE
Horrid Henry and the Purple Hand Gang ruling the world.

SECRET DREAM
Beating Henry at Gotcha – every time.

Aerobic Al

WORST NIGHTMARE
Being chased – and not being able to run away fast enough.

SECRET DREAM
Winning at the Olympics.

Greedy Graham

WORST NIGHTMARE
A world without sweets.

SECRET DREAM
Winning his weight in chocolate.

Rabid Rebecca

WORST NIGHTMARE
Being attacked by a spider and – even worse – having to babysit for Henry again.

SECRET DREAM
Babysitting for kids who do as they're told and go to bed at five o'clock.

Rude Ralph

WORST NIGHTMARE
Being banished from the Purple Hand Gang and forced to join Moody Margaret's Secret Club.

SECRET DREAM
Beating the World Record for the Biggest Burp ever.

Stuck-Up Steve

WORST NIGHTMARE
Discovering that all his zillions of expensive new toys really belong to Henry.

SECRET DREAM
Scaring Henry so much that he never comes to stay again.

Horrid Henry's Nightmare Birthday Party

HAPPY BIRTHDAY HENRY

Horrid Henry dreams that his mean, horrible parents are planning the worst party ever.

ENTERTAINMENT

- A walk in the countryside with a nice healthy picnic
    The countryside smells.

- A swimming party with special guest Soggy Sid
    I hate swimming!

- A lovely meal out at the ~~Virtuous Veggie~~ Gobble and Go

- A trip of a lifetime to the ~~fantastic~~ theme park — Book World most-boring-ever-invented

- A night out to the Daffy and her Dancing Daisies concert
    I want to go and see the Killer Boy Rats instead and it's MY birthday!

GRISLY GUESTS

That Worm is NOT invited

- ✗ Perfect Peter NO!
- ✗ Moody Margaret NO!
- ✗ Sour Susan NO!
- ✗ Stuck-up Steve NO!
- ✗ Bossy Bill NO!
- ✗ Lisping Lily Please NO!

Old misery-guts Margaret CAN'T come.

22

FOUL FOOD

- Carrot and celery sticks with yoghurt dip
- Fruit salad - apples, melons, oranges, bananas
- Yoghurt with gooseberries
- Lettuce and tomato sandwiches
- Veggie stew with cabbage
- Carrot cake

BLECCCCHHH!

TOP FIVE PARTY RULES

1. Say thank you for EVERY present — even if it isn't exactly what you want
2. Let guests win ALL the games
3. Be nice to your guests
4. Fill your plate with healthy food and eat it all up — DON'T hide it in a drawer
5. Be kind to your little brother and let him join in

Call this a party? The whole point of a birthday is that everyone has to do whatever I say and buy me exactly what I want.

PARTY GAMES

Pass the Parcel (prize — ~~a granola bar~~)
Mega-Whirl Goo-Shooter

Pin the tail on the pink ~~fluffy bunny~~
Make Fluffy into a mummy with loo roll

Musical Statues (to Daffy and her Dancing Daisies
That stupid music won't be allowed at my party. It's got to be Killer Boy Rats and Driller Cannibals!

JUST A THOUGHT...

Maybe a no gifts policy this year and ask all the guests to give money to charity instead?

This can't be real. It must be a nightmare. WAKE ME UP, QUICK!

23

Perfect Peter's Pirate Party

"MUUUMMM!" wailed PETER. "Henry's trying to scare me!"

"What's going on?" said Mum.

"Henry said I'm going to turn into a shrunken head if I have a pirate party."

"Henry, don't be horrid," said Mum, glaring. "Peter, there's no such thing."

"Told you, Henry," said Perfect Peter.

"If I were you I'd have a Sammy the Slug party," said Horrid Henry.

"Sammy the *Snail*," said Peter. "I'm having a pirate party and you can't stop me. So there."

Rats, thought Horrid Henry. How could he make Peter change his mind?

"Don't dooooooo it, Peter," Henry howled spookily under Peter's door every night. "Beware! Beware!"

"Stop it, Henry!" screamed Peter

"You'll be sorry," Horrid Henry scrawled all over Peter's homework.

"Remember the cannibal curse," Henry whispered over supper the night before the party.

"Henry, leave your brother alone or you won't be coming to the party," said Mum.

Is Horrid Henry allowed to go to Perfect Peter's pirate party, and does the cannibal curse come true? Find out in **'Perfect Peter's Pirate Party'** in **Horrid Henry Robs the Bank.**

Pirate Party Time

Everyone enjoys the treasure hunt at Perfect Peter's pirate party until an uninvited guest turns up. Follow the time clues, write the letters in the answer spaces below and find out who it is.

Where does the big hand go when it's ...

1. Five o'clock?
2. Twenty to six?
3. Quarter past five?
4. Ten to six?
5. Twenty past five?
6. Half past five?

7. Ten past five?
8. Quarter to six?
9. Five past five?
10. Five past five?
11. Twenty-five to six?

12. Ten past five?
13. Five past five?
14. Twenty to six?
15. Quarter to six?

16. Ten past five?
17. Five past five?
18. Ten past five?

ANSWER: _ _ _ _ _ _ _ _ _ _ _ _ _ _ _ _ _ _ _

What Do Your Nightmares Reveal About You?

1. **If your favourite dream turned into a nightmare, which of these three options would it be?**

   (a) You've just won loads of cold hard cash and can't wait to spend it all – then your parents put it all in the bank to save until you're grown up.
   (b) You're the Prime Minister and everyone obeys you – but then your best friend becomes Prime Minster instead and throws you into jail.
   (c) You're walking through a meadow full of lovely flowers with your mum, but when you pick a bunch of flowers for her, she gets cross and tells you off.

3. **In your nightmare, you're being chased – but who is chasing you?**

   (a) A very angry teacher.
   (b) A mean best friend you don't like any more.
   (c) A scary pirate who chops people's heads off.

2. **You're having a nightmare about school. Which of these is most likely?**

   (a) Your horrible teacher has given you hours and hours of homework.
   (b) You aren't captain of the school football team any more – in fact, you're not even on the team.
   (c) You haven't got any gold stars in the Good as Gold Book.

4. **You're all alone in a nightmarish place. Where is it?**

   (a) In a muddy field in the countryside, surrounded by fierce bulls.
   (b) In your enemies' den, with no one to boss about.
   (c) In a very noisy, brightly-lit restaurant, like Gobble and Go.

5. A ghost is haunting your dreams. What is it like?

(a) A great big spooky bunny with no tail and huge teeth coming to get you.

(b) A screeching ghoul with blood dripping from its mouth.

(c) A misty graveyard ghost moaning and wailing.

6. A monster is coming towards you in your nightmare. Is it …

(a) A zombie vampire werewolf?

(b) A creepy acid alien?

(c) A hairy scary monster with big claws?

7. You're having the worst nightmare ever! What is it?

(a) Crisps, sweets and chocolate are banned – for the rest of your life.

(b) You never win at anything ever again.

(c) You've lost your favourite cuddly toy.

8. Your nightmare is so scary, it wakes you up. What do you do?

(a) Quickly hide under the covers.

(b) Scream very loudly, then go straight back to sleep.

(c) Run crying to Mum and Dad's room.

Count up how many (a)s, (b)s and (c)s you've chosen, then check below to see what your score reveals about you.

Mostly (a)s: Like Horrid Henry, you hate school, teachers and homework. You're secretly scared of spooks, vampires and zombies – but you're even more scared of losing all your pocket money and sweets.

Mostly (b)s: Like Moody Margaret, you love being in charge. You're a teeny-tiny bit scared of ghouls and aliens, but your biggest nightmare is being a loser and somebody else bossing you about!

Mostly (c)s: Like Perfect Peter, you want to be as good as gold. You're scared of monsters, ghosts and pirates – but you're even more terrified of being told off!

Mother's Day
Survival Guide

When Horrid Henry finds out what Perfect Peter is planning for Mother's Day, he's determined to steal Peter's ideas and claim all the credit. Here's his guide to surviving the day.

Breakfast in bed

Goody goody wormy worm Peter is planning to take Mum breakfast in bed, but I'm fed up of him always outdoing me. This year, things are going to be different.

- I'll get up really early and make Mum the best breakfast she's ever eaten - soft-boiled eggs, toast, jam, juice and tea. Just imagine the look on Peter's face when he brings up Mum's breakfast tray and sees her already tucking into my yummalicious treats.
- If Perfect Peter still manages to be up before me, I'll tell him Dad wants to talk to him, then throw his toast away and make my own.
- Race to prepare the breakfast. It doesn't matter what it looks like – just that I get there before Peter! Push Peter out of the way and run up the stairs to reach Mum first.

Card

Last year Peter spent ages making Mum a giant sparkly hand-painted card, but I've got a better idea:

- Buy a card. It will be much better than any home-made monstrosity Peter has painted. (Much quicker than making one too.)
- If there are no cards left, don't panic. Get a cheap birthday card instead and cross out the words on the front.

Presents

Peter always buys Mum a huge bunch of flowers and a present, but I'm not spending my hard-earned pocket money on a stupid present. I'm going to:

- Pick flowers from the garden - they are free and Mum probably won't even notice. And I'll make sure it's a much bigger bunch than Peter's. Tee hee.

- Make some coupons. This is a great gift and it won't cost a penny. Mum doesn't know how lucky she is, having me as her son!
- Write a poem. Mum will like that much better because she'll know I've put loads of time and effort into it instead of just going to the shops like Peter.

Mum is going to be SO grateful. I bet she'll let me watch TV all day and give me loads of crisps, sweets and chocolates – and extra pocket money so I can buy the latest Robomatic Supersonic Space Howler Deluxe. RESULT!

Scruffs Pet Show Puzzle

At Scruffs, the neighbourhood pet show, there's a prize for the pet that looks most like its owner. Match these pets to their owners. Who do you think should win the prize?

2 Speedy, the fit and fast greyhound.

1 Fluffy, fast asleep as usual.

3 Fattie, the enormous guinea pig.

4 Grumpy, the bad-tempered pug dog.

5 Snore, the snoozy rabbit.

6 Piddle, the dancing poodle.

7 Baby Jane, the lovely little Yorkie dog.

A Aerobic Al,
the fastest boy
in the school.

B Lazy Linda,
who loves to
snooze.

C Greedy Graham,
the greediest boy in
the school.

D Sour Susan,
What a grump!

E Miss Battle-Axe,
who surprises
everyone at the
pet show!

F Horrid Henry,
enjoying himself.

G Miss Lovely,
Perfect Peter's
lovely teacher.

WRITE YOUR ANSWERS HERE:
1=
2=
3=
4=
5=
6=
7=
Who's your winner?

Comical Creatures Criss-cross

Can you fit the words below into the criss-cross puzzle AND use them to complete the punchlines for the animal jokes?

3 letters
PAT
VET

7 letters
PENGUIN
FINGERS
SPOTTED
LETTUCE
CHEETAH

4 letters
FEET

6 letters
CARROT

CLUE:
FILL IN THE 4-LETTER WORD FIRST AND THE 3-LETTER WORDS LAST!

Comical Creatures Missing Words

WHAT DO YOU GET IF YOU SIT UNDER A COW?

A __ __ __ ON THE HEAD.

WHAT'S BRIGHT ORANGE AND SOUNDS LIKE A PARROT?

A __ __ __ __ __ __!

WHAT'S BLACK AND WHITE AND BLACK AND WHITE AND BLACK AND WHITE?

A __ __ __ __ __ __ __ ROLLING DOWN A HILL.

WHY DO GIRAFFES HAVE LONG NECKS?

BECAUSE THEIR __ __ __ __ STINK.

WHY DO GORILLAS HAVE BIG NOSTRILS?

BECAUSE THEY HAVE BIG __ __ __ __ __ __ __ .

WHAT'S THE BEST WAY TO CATCH A RABBIT?

HIDE IN THE BUSHES AND MAKE A NOISE LIKE __ __ __ __ __ __ __ __ .

WHY CAN'T A LEOPARD HIDE?

BECAUSE HE'S ALWAYS __ __ __ __ __ __ .

WHAT KIND OF ANIMAL ALWAYS WINS AT GOTCHA?

A __ __ __ __ __ __ __ .

DOCTOR, DOCTOR, I FEEL LIKE A DOG!

THEN GO AND SEE A __ __ __ !

Horrid Henry's April Fools' Day Finger Trick

Horrid Henry loves fooling his friends on April Fools' Day. Here's his special spooky finger trick!

You will need

- A small cardboard box with a lid (if your mum buys some jewellery, ask her to save the box for you)
- Paper and pen
- Glue or sticky tape
- Scissors
- Cotton wool
- Ketchup for a bloody finger or talcum powder for a mummy finger

What to do

1. Cover the top of the lid with white paper using glue or sticky tape. On the top of the box, write bloody finger or mummy finger – try to make your writing look old and spooky.
2. Cut a hole in the bottom of the box, big enough to fit your middle finger through.
3. Push your finger through the hole and put some cotton wool around it.
4. For bloody finger, squirt in a small amount of ketchup. Or for mummy finger, dampen your finger and cover with talcum powder.
5. Put the lid on the box – and prepare to scare!
6. Hold the box, keeping your finger in place.
7. Tell your friend you've got something to show them, and ask them to open the box.
8. Ask if they want to touch the finger and, as they do, lift up your finger suddenly… and listen to them scream!

34

Poltergeist Puzzle

A sneaky poltergeist is up to mischief in Perfect Peter's tidy bedroom. Take a good look at Peter's room on the page BEFORE the poltergeist gets up to its tricks, then turn the page and see if you can spot the 10 differences.

Poltergeist Puzzle

Now look again. Can you circle the 10 differences without looking back at page 35?

Spot the Spooky Easter Bunnies

Horrid Henry has nightmares about a spooky bunny without a tail. How many spooky bunnies can you spot below?

Win Your Weight in Chocolate Competition

Shop 'n' Drop are holding a competition, and the winner will receive their own weight in chocolate. Just imagine if any of the eight characters or animals below won the competition! The heaviest would win the most chocolate and the lightest would win the least.

A. Fang –
Horrid Henry's hamster

B. An elephant

C. Greasy Greta –
the gigantic dinner lady who scoffs all the lunchtime treats

D. Greedy Graham –
who loves his grub

E. Moody Margaret –
thin and mean

F. A spooky graveyard ghost

G. The biggest, scariest spider ever

H. Fluffy the fat cat –
who loves to eat and sleep

Can you put them all in order from heaviest to lightest?

		Write your answer below
HEAVIEST	1	
	2	
	3	
↓	4	
	5	
	6	
	7	
LIGHTEST	8	

Horrid Henry's Great Escape

Horrid Henry's mum and dad's idea of a good holiday is all the things Henry hates – camping in a muddy field, horrible hikes in the countryside, trips to crumbly old castles and boring museums, and being forced to swim in the freezing sea. This year, Henry is going to do everything he can to escape . . .

Remind Mum and Dad how horrible last year's holiday was. I'll tell them that Rude Ralph and his family are going on a theme park holiday and I think that's a great idea too.

Pretend to be sick. Mum and Dad will have to cancel the holiday. (Just be careful you don't use this excuse if you want to do something else fun later, as your mean, horrible parents will probably make you stay at home.)

Throw a tantrum. I won't stop until Mum and Dad promise to take me to a theme park and never go camping again.

Write a fake letter. I'll write a letter from the campsite owner pretending that a herd of fierce bulls have been let loose in the field and the campsite has been closed – all summer.

If none of that works, I'll...

Hide the car key.
After everyone has searched for hours, I'll pretend to find the key under the sofa. Mum and Dad will reward me with lots of sweets and extra pocket money. But it'll be far too late to go on holiday by then and we'll have to stay at home.

Leave my suitcase at home.
Mum and Dad will have to drive all the way back again and by the time we get to the campsite the holiday will be nearly over.

Be extra horrid!
I'll argue with Perfect Peter, and scream loudly in the back of the car. Mum and Dad will get so fed up that they won't want to take me on holiday at all. I might even get to go away with Rude Ralph instead.

Delay on the way.
I'll demand a stop on the way and pretend to be locked in the toilet. By the time the door has been chopped down, it'll be too late to carry on.

Best Beach Games

Horrid Henry hates the cold sea, so if he can't escape a trip to the seaside, he gets some beach games going (then there's no time left for swimming, ha ha!).

SANDCASTLE CONTEST

You will need

2 or more players
A bucket and spade per player

How to play:

1. Mark two lines in the sand – about 20 steps apart.
2. Put the buckets and spades on one of the lines.
3. The players stand on the other line (the start line).
4. One player shouts 'GO!' The players run and collect their buckets, run back and put their buckets down on the start line, then run and get their spades.
5. Each player makes a sandcastle as quickly as possible.
6. The winner is the first person to finish their sandcastle – but if it falls apart when they remove the bucket, the second person is the winner.

BURY YOUR LITTLE BROTHER OR SISTER

You will need

A spade
One little brother or sister

How to play:

1. Tell your little brother to lie very still on the sand.
2. Cover him from his feet up to his neck with sand.
3. Pat it all down so he can't escape. Tee hee!

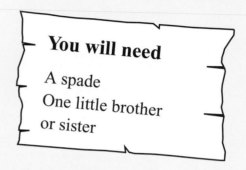

Summer Sudoku

Fill in the sudoku so that every square and row – both up and down – contains the four pictures shown.

Too easy-peasy for you? Try a trickier one! Fill in every square and row with numbers 1-6.

The Purple Hand Gang Mystery

In the school holidays, Horrid Henry sneaks into the Secret Club den, pinches Moody Margaret's Chocolate Fudge Chewies and hides them in the Purple Hand fort. But when Henry returns to the fort later, the biscuits have gone! All that's left is a note in a mysterious code. Can you help Henry solve the mystery and catch the thief?

1. Suspects and Motives

Horrid Henry makes a list of the 6 most likely suspects and their motives – but he muddles them up.

SUSPECTS	MOTIVES
1 Perfect Peter	**A** Not sure what his motive is, but he can run away very fast.
2 Mum	**B** Loves scoffing Chocolate Fudge Chewies as much as me.
3 Greedy Graham	**C** Revenge of the Secret Club – and she wants her biscuits back.
4 Aerobic Al	**D** Wants me to eat healthy fruit and vegetables. Yeuch!
5 Moody Margaret	**E** A member of the Purple Hand Gang – he wanted to get his share of the loot.
6 Rude Ralph	**F** He's a little worm and cries when he can't be in the Purple Hand Gang.

Can you match the motives to the suspects? Write your answers (A-F) below:

1 Perfect Peter = **MOTIVE** ___   4 Aerobic Al = **MOTIVE** ___

2 Mum = **MOTIVE** ___   5 Moody Margaret = **MOTIVE** ___

3 Greedy Graham = **MOTIVE** ___   6 Rude Ralph = **MOTIVE** ___

2. The Clues

Henry thinks that the best 3 motives in order are **C, E** and **F.** Using your answers, find the top 3 suspects and write their names in the boxes below. Then from the clues provided, work out how long each suspect spent in Henry's garden on the day of the robbery and what they were doing.

TOP THREE SUSPECTS	HOW LONG?	DOING WHAT?
1		
2		
3		

WHERE: 10 minutes, 30 minutes, 45 minutes
DOING WHAT: Helping Dad, Playing Pirates, Hiding in the Fort

CLUES: 1. SUSPECT 2 spent less time in the garden than SUSPECT 1.
2. Helping Dad took 45 minutes.
3. SUSPECT 1 was playing pirates.

3. The Code Letter

Henry is still confused! And then – HOORAY! – he finds the code-cracking formula lying in the grass outside the fort. It's time to crack the code and read the note. You can find the code-cracking formula on page 46.

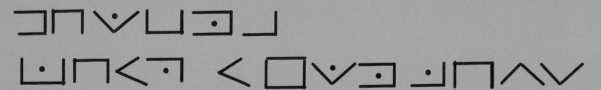

Write your answer here:

_ _ _ _ _ _ _

_ _ _ _ _ _ _ _ _ _ _

Now can you guess who pinched the Chocolate Fudge Chewies?

Write your final answer here: _____

The Special Secret Code

Here is the code-cracker for the mysterious secret code. Draw two grids – one like a noughts and crosses grid and the other one like a big X. Then fill in the letters of the alphabet as shown below.

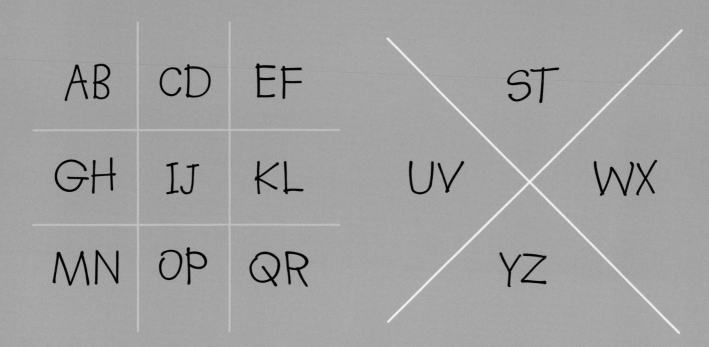

To write in code, draw the grid lines that are around the letter, adding in a dot for the second letter within the lines. Be careful to put the dot in the right place or your friends won't be able to read your secret messages.

For example, an E looks like a capital L shape. An R looks like an upside down capital L shape with a dot added.

So Henry in code looks like this:

Peter in code looks like this:

| Can you write your name in code? |

Horrible Homework

Back at school, Miss Battle-Axe gets a shock when Henry writes his essay in his new favourite code. Miss Battle-Axe can't read it – can you?

What has Henry written for his horrible homework?

_____

_____

_____

_____

_____

_____

Match the Badge

It's a big surprise when Mrs Oddbod asks Henry to be the school's Healthy Food Monitor. Henry's favourite words are sweets, crisps and chocolate! Imagine if Mrs Oddbod picked the wrong person for everything. Can you match the characters below to the WRONG badge?

THE WRONG BADGE IS:

LAZY LINDA
She's often caught snoring in class.

_____

RUDE RALPH
He never says "please" or "thank you".

_____

MOODY MARGARET
She's always falling out with her best friend, Sour Susan.

_____

BEEFY BERT
His answer to every question is "I dunno".

_____

HORRID HENRY
Loves eating sweets, crisps and chocolate.

_____

BABBLING BOB
He talks non-stop in class.

_____

AEROBIC AL
The fastest runner in school.

_____

WEEPY WILLIAM
He's always bursting into tears at school.

_____

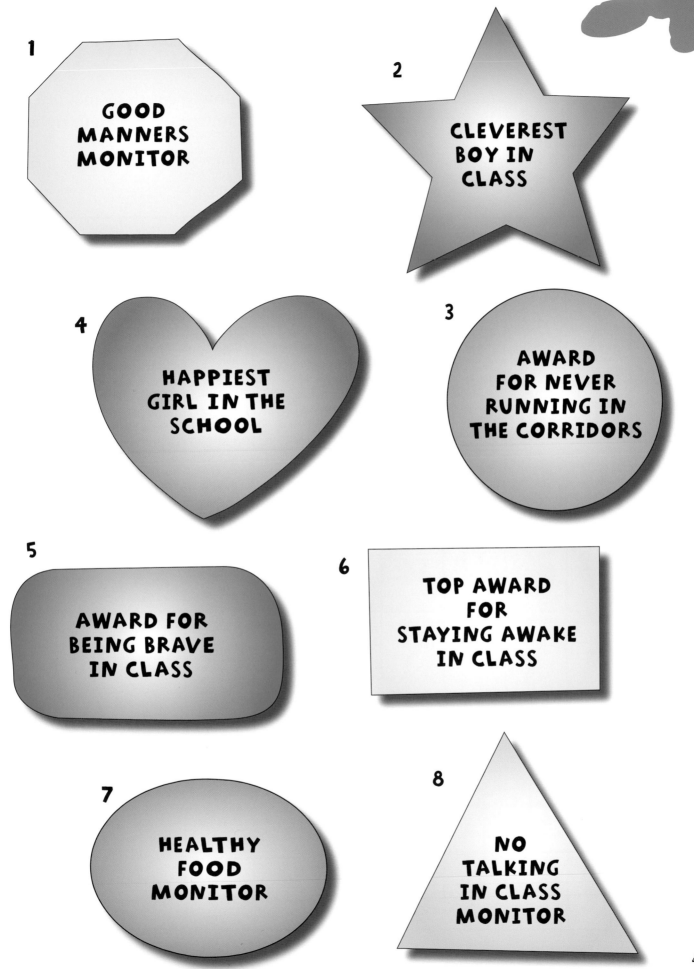

1 GOOD MANNERS MONITOR

2 CLEVEREST BOY IN CLASS

4 HAPPIEST GIRL IN THE SCHOOL

3 AWARD FOR NEVER RUNNING IN THE CORRIDORS

5 AWARD FOR BEING BRAVE IN CLASS

6 TOP AWARD FOR STAYING AWAKE IN CLASS

7 HEALTHY FOOD MONITOR

8 NO TALKING IN CLASS MONITOR

49

Chase the Chocolate Maze

Find your way through this picture maze to the chocolate. Follow the path by moving along the squares that contain carrots or sprouts. Move one square at a time, left, right, up or down, but not diagonally.

Start ↓

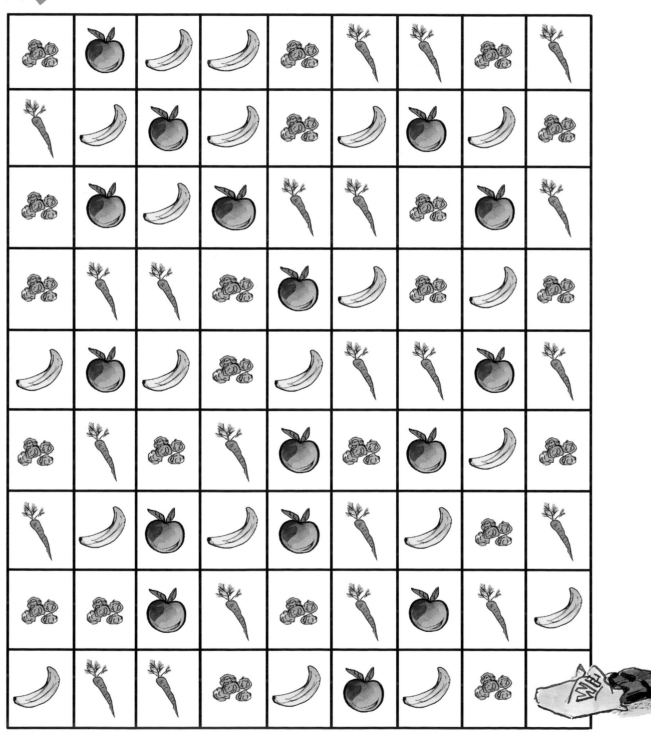

50

Greasy Greta's Sneaky Snacks

Greasy Greta the Demon Dinner Lady sneaks all the kids' favourite snacks from their school packed lunches. Can you find the snacks below in the wordsearch puzzle? The leftover letters spell out 6 snacks that are left after Greasy Greta's gone.

CRISPS   TOFFEES   FUDGE
DOUGHNUT   BISCUITS   FIZZYWIZZ
CHOCOLATE   SWEETS   MUFFIN

S	T	I	U	C	S	I	B	E	F
T	O	F	C	A	R	R	T	O	I
E	F	U	T	Y	O	A	G	H	Z
E	F	D	U	R	L	T	O	R	Z
W	E	G	A	O	N	G	E	R	Y
S	E	E	C	R	I	S	P	S	W
A	S	O	M	U	F	F	I	N	I
I	H	S	I	N	S	A	P	P	Z
C	T	U	N	H	G	U	O	D	Z
L	E	C	U	C	U	M	B	E	R

Fill in the hidden words here:

_____ _____ _____

_____ _____ _____

51

Greedy Graham's Grub

Greedy Graham isn't happy when school becomes a sweet-free zone. He sneaks his own tasty treats into his lunchbox. Why not try making some too? Just don't let Miss Battle-Axe catch you!

Rainbow Balls

You will need

A big bowl

A wooden spoon

25g cocoa powder

50g icing sugar

50g chopped nuts (if you like nuts!)

50g cream cheese

Hundreds and thousands

What to do:

1. Put the cream cheese, icing sugar, cocoa powder and chopped nuts into a bowl.

2. Stir everything up into a cheesy, choccy glop.

3. Roll the mixture into little balls, about the size of a gobstopper.

4. Sprinkle the hundreds and thousands onto a plate or board.

5. Roll the choccy balls in the hundreds and thousands until they are covered all over.

6. Pop them on a plate and keep in the fridge until you are ready to eat them.

Coconut Cubes

You will need

Two big bowls

A fork

A cake tin (lined with greaseproof paper)

397g tin of condensed milk

400g icing sugar

350g desiccated coconut

Pink food colouring

What to do

1. Put the condensed milk and icing sugar into one of the bowls and mix them together with a fork. Then add the desiccated coconut and mix in too.

2. Take half of the mixture out of the bowl and set aside in the other bowl.

3. Colour the mixture in the first bowl with a few drops of food colouring and mix with your hands to make sure the colour spreads properly.

4. Put the coloured half of the mixture into the lined cake tin, and pat it down with your hands until flat on top.

5. Very important! Wash your hands to get rid of all the food colouring.

6. Now put the white half of the mixture on top of the coloured layer and pat it down with your hands until flat. Leave overnight, then cut into small squares.

Hallowe'en Criss-cross

3 letters
BAT
BOO
FUN
WEB

4 letters
MASK

5 letters
NIGHT
PARTY
SCARY
SPOOK
TREAT
TRICK
WITCH

6 letters
SPIDER
SWEETS

7 letters
COSTUME
OCTOBER
PUMPKIN

CLUE: FILL IN THE 4-LETTER WORD FIRST.

54

A Horrid Hallowe'en Game

Henry likes playing spooky games on Hallowe'en – especially if he wins lots of sweets. Here's his favourite game of all.

Melt Miss Battle-Axe

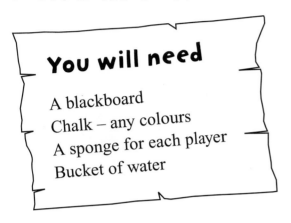

You will need

A blackboard
Chalk – any colours
A sponge for each player
Bucket of water

What to do

1. Draw a picture of Miss Battle-Axe on the blackboard using the chalk.
2. Fill the bucket with water.
3. In turn, each player puts their sponge in the water, squeezes it out and throws it at the blackboard.
4. As Miss Battle-Axe gets wet, she starts to look as if she's melting.
5. When Henry's scary teacher has completely melted away, everyone is a winner!

Horrid Henry's Ghost Guide

Here are a few of the ghosts you are likely to meet as you fearlessly prowl into dark cupboards and search beneath creaky beds and behind rattling doors. Remember: all ghosts are terrified of the phrase, "Be gone, worms!"

1. Graveyard ghouls

2. Alien acid monsters

3. Clanking, headless knights

4. Great-aunts in rocking chairs

5. Margaret the frog ghost

6. Zombie mummies

7. Vampire chickens

8. Injection bunnies (scariest of all)

Top Spooks!

You've met Horrid Henry's top spooks – now it's time to play Top Spooks! Copy and cut out the 8 cards shown in this spread, then create your own ghosts and ghouls to add to the mix too.

VAMPIRE CHICKEN

SIZE	3
NOISE	8
SCARY SCALE	9

GRAVEYARD GHOUL

SIZE	8
NOISE	9
SCARY SCALE	6

CLANKING HEADLESS KNIGHT

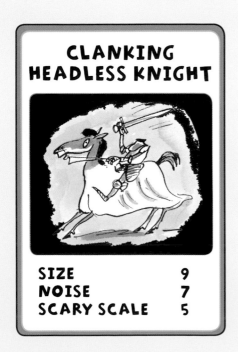

SIZE	9
NOISE	7
SCARY SCALE	5

MARGARET THE FROG GHOST

SIZE	5
NOISE	10
SCARY SCALE	5

GREAT-AUNT IN ROCKING CHAIR

SIZE	6
NOISE	6
SCARY SCALE	3

ALIEN ACID MONSTER

SIZE	7
NOISE	5
SCARY SCALE	7

INJECTION BUNNY

SIZE	4
NOISE	3
SCARY SCALE	10

ZOMBIE MUMMY

SIZE	10
NOISE	4
SCARY SCALE	8

How to play *Top Spooks*

1. Deal the cards out between yourself and the other player so that you have the same number. Keep your cards in front of you, face down on the table.

2. Both players pick up their top card at the same time.

3. The first player reads out one of the scores on their card. Try to choose the score that you think could beat the other player. For example, if your spook has a scary scale of 8, say 'Scary Scale 8'.

4. If the other player has a spook with a scary scale lower than 8, they hand over their card to you. If their spook has a scary scale of 9 or 10, you hand your card to them. Whoever wins that round puts both the cards at the bottom of their pile.

5. The game continues until one of the players has taken all the cards, and wins the game.

Would You Make a Good Ghost Hunter?

Have you got what it takes to hunt ghosts? Follow the arrows and find out!

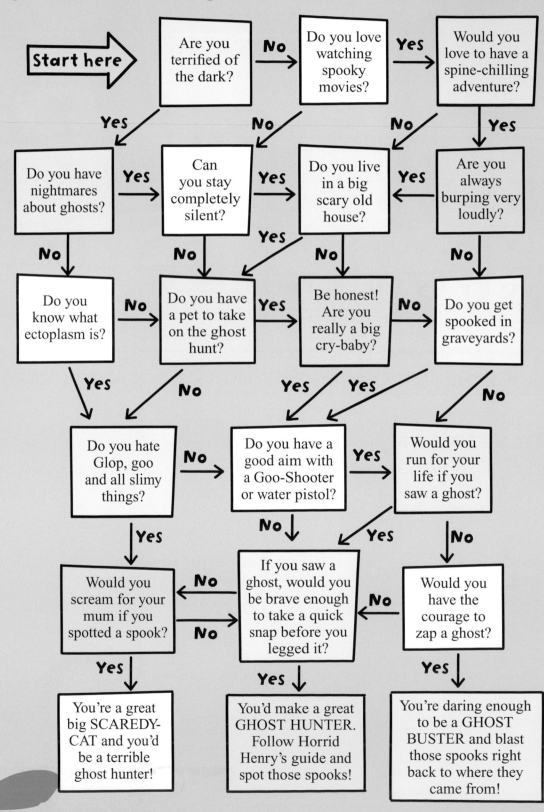

Start here →

Are you terrified of the dark? — **No** → Do you love watching spooky movies? — **Yes** → Would you love to have a spine-chilling adventure?

Are you terrified of the dark? — **Yes** ↓

Do you love watching spooky movies? — **No** ↓

Would you love to have a spine-chilling adventure? — **No** ↓ / **Yes** ↓

Do you have nightmares about ghosts? — **Yes** → Can you stay completely silent? — **Yes** → Do you live in a big scary old house?

Are you always burping very loudly? — **Yes** → Do you live in a big scary old house?

Do you have nightmares about ghosts? — **No** ↓

Can you stay completely silent? — **No** ↓

Do you live in a big scary old house? — **Yes** ↓ / **No** ↓

Are you always burping very loudly? — **No** ↓

Do you know what ectoplasm is? — **No** → Do you have a pet to take on the ghost hunt? — **Yes** → Be honest! Are you really a big cry-baby? — **No** → Do you get spooked in graveyards?

Do you know what ectoplasm is? — **Yes** ↓

Do you have a pet to take on the ghost hunt? — **No** ↓

Be honest! Are you really a big cry-baby? — **Yes** ↓ / **Yes** ↓

Do you get spooked in graveyards? — **No** ↓

Do you hate Glop, goo and all slimy things? — **No** → Do you have a good aim with a Goo-Shooter or water pistol? — **Yes** → Would you run for your life if you saw a ghost?

Do you hate Glop, goo and all slimy things? — **Yes** ↓

Do you have a good aim with a Goo-Shooter or water pistol? — **No** ↓

Would you run for your life if you saw a ghost? — **Yes** ↓ / **No** ↓

Would you scream for your mum if you spotted a spook? — **No** ← If you saw a ghost, would you be brave enough to take a quick snap before you legged it? — **No** → Would you have the courage to zap a ghost?

Would you scream for your mum if you spotted a spook? — **No** ← If you saw a ghost...

Would you scream for your mum if you spotted a spook? — **Yes** ↓

If you saw a ghost, would you be brave enough to take a quick snap before you legged it? — **Yes** ↓

Would you have the courage to zap a ghost? — **Yes** ↓

You're a great big SCAREDY-CAT and you'd be a terrible ghost hunter!

You'd make a great GHOST HUNTER. Follow Horrid Henry's guide and spot those spooks!

You're daring enough to be a GHOST BUSTER and blast those spooks right back to where they came from!

Weird Wordsearch

Can you find these nightmare names in the wordsearch puzzle below? Search up, down, left, right and diagonally.

POLTERGEIST   ZOMBIE   PHANTOM
GHOST   MONSTER   SKELETON
SPOOK   ALIEN   MUMMY

T	Z	Y	V	E	S	J	R	C	G	J
H	S	B	M	P	R	E	Q	C	N	W
P	Y	I	O	M	T	J	A	O	O	F
I	V	O	E	S	U	G	W	G	T	H
L	K	F	N	G	Z	M	I	H	E	T
L	B	O	Z	B	R	W	M	O	L	C
W	M	Q	P	O	S	E	K	S	E	L
M	N	X	H	U	M	Y	T	T	K	M
G	K	E	X	U	L	B	H	L	S	G
N	E	I	L	A	X	X	I	U	O	K
P	H	A	N	T	O	M	Y	E	M	P

Horrid Henry's Haunted House

Henry lay in bed. Somehow he'd survived the dreadful meal and Stuck-up Steve's bragging about his expensive clothes, toys and trainers. Now here he was, alone in the attic at the top of the house. He'd jumped into bed, carefully avoiding the faded brown patch on the floor. He was sure it was just spilled cola or something, but just in case… Henry looked around him. The only thing he didn't like was the huge wardrobe opposite the bed. It loomed up in the darkness at him. You could hide a body in that wardrobe, thought Henry, then rather wished he hadn't.

"Oooooooooh."

Henry stiffened.

Had he just imagined the sound of someone moaning?

Silence.

Nothing, thought Henry, snuggling down under the covers. Just the wind.

"Oooooooooh."

This time the moaning was a fraction louder. The hairs on Henry's neck stood up. He gripped the sheets tightly.

"Haaaaaahhhhhhh."

Henry sat up.

"Haaaaaaaaahhhhhhhhhhhh."

The ghostly breathy moaning sound was not coming from outside. It appeared to be coming from inside the giant wardrobe.

Quickly, Henry switched on the bedside light.

What am I going to do? thought Henry. He wanted to run screaming to his aunt.

But the truth was, Henry was too frightened to move.

Does Henry dare to find out what's in the wardrobe? Find out in **'Horrid Henry's Haunted House'** from **Horrid Henry's Haunted House**.

62

Nightmare Maze

Help Horrid Henry find his way out of the haunted house.
If you bump into a spook, you've gone the wrong way!

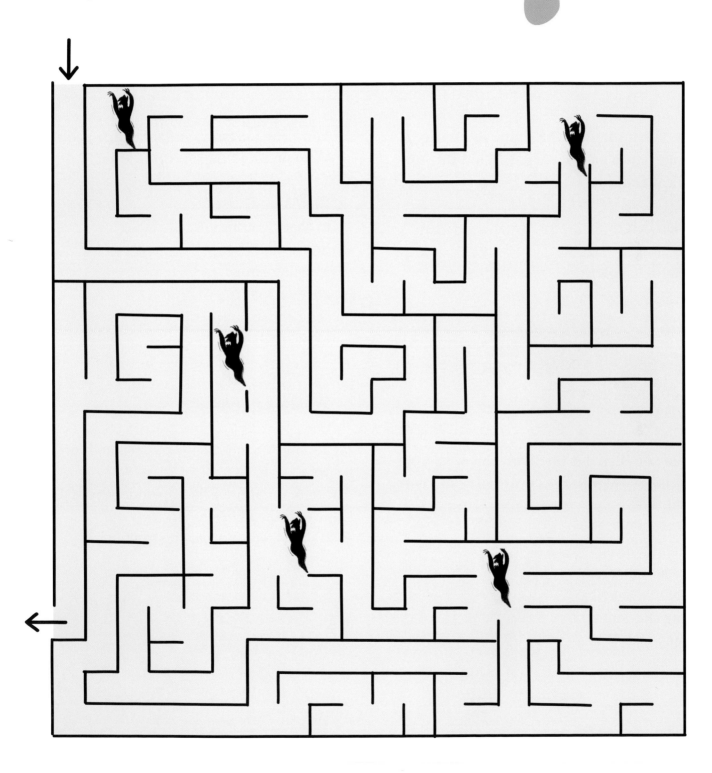

Could You Survive a Night in a Haunted House?

1. **Before you turn off the light, you notice a strange stain on the carpet. What do you think it could be?**

(a) Spilled cola.
(b) Fake blood.
(c) A vaporized ghost.

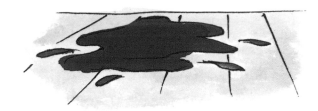

3. **When you turn out the light, you see a huge looming shadow in the corner of your room. What is it?**

(a) The wardrobe.
(b) A trick of the light.
(c) Something horrible hiding and waiting to get you.

2. **You hear footsteps outside your room. Who or what do you think it is?**

(a) Rich Aunt Ruby coming to check you're OK.
(b) Stuck-up Steve creeping about.
(c) A ghost looking for someone to scare.

4. **Your duvet twitches and makes you jump. What's happened?**

(a) You must have dropped asleep and moved in your sleep.
(b) Stuck-up Steve is hiding under the bed pulling at your duvet.
(c) It's a poltergeist causing trouble.

5. You hear a moaning sound outside the window. Is it …

(a) The wind?
(b) Rich Aunt Ruby's cat?
(c) Ghosts from the nearby graveyard?

6. You hear a blood-curdling scream from downstairs. What do you think it is?

(a) Someone screaming on the TV.
(b) Stuck-up Steve being a scaredy-cat.
(c) A ghoul attacking its first victim before it comes to get you.

7. The bedroom door starts creaking open and a big white shape appears. Is it …

(a) Rich Aunt Ruby in her white dressing-gown coming to say goodnight?
(b) Stuck-up Steve dressed up as a ghost in a white sheet?
(c) A ghoul ready to pounce on you?

8. It really is a ghoul, wailing, moaning and coming to get you. What do you do?

(a) Nothing. You've been fast asleep for ages.
(b) Leap out of bed bravely and attack it with your Goo-Shooter.
(c) Run screaming from the room.

Count how many (a)s, (b)s and (c)s you've scored.

Mostly (a)s: You're calm and clever and you don't believe in ghosts. Sleeping in a haunted house doesn't scare you at all. You can certainly survive the night – unless you discover you're wrong and the ghouls really do come to get you!

Mostly (b)s: You believe in ghosts a bit, but you think it's more likely to be Stuck-up Steve playing tricks and trying to scare you. You'll survive the night – unless it turns out not to be Steve after all!

Mostly (c)s: You're best staying safely at home. You're scared of every shadow and every little sound and you wouldn't survive in a haunted house for five minutes – and definitely not a whole night on your own!

Horrid Henry's Nightmare Christmas

This is the Christmas I hope I never, EVER have . . .

★ No presents except a pencil set, socks, and bubble bath.

★ The only TV shows are repeats of Daffy and her Dancing Daisies and Nellie's Nursery.

★ Christmas lunch is just sprouts.

★ Stuck-up Steve is staying over.

Great Aunt Greta sends me a pink, sparkling handbag and Peter £25.

Moody Margaret comes over to brag about all the toys and loot she got.

The fortune inside my cracker says, "You are so lucky to have such a wonderful brother."

Horrid Henry's Ambush

Horrid Henry woke with a jolt.

AAARRGGH! He'd fallen asleep. How could he? Panting and gasping Henry switched on the light. Phew. His traps were intact. His stocking was empty. Father Christmas hadn't been yet.

Wow, was that lucky. That was incredibly lucky. Henry lay back, his heart pounding.

And then Horrid Henry had a terrible thought.

What if Father Christmas had decided to be spiteful and *avoid* Henry's bedroom this year? Or what if he'd played a sneaky trick on Henry and filled a stocking *downstairs* instead?

Nah. No way.

But wait. When Father Christmas came to Rude Ralph's house he always filled the stockings downstairs. Now Henry came to think of it, Moody Margaret always left her stocking downstairs too, hanging from the fireplace, not from the end of her bed, like Henry did.

Horrid Henry looked at the clock. It was past midnight. Mum and Dad had forbidden him to go downstairs till morning, on pain of having all his presents taken away and no telly all day.

But this was an emergency. He'd creep downstairs, take a quick peek to make sure he hadn't missed Father Christmas, then be back in bed in a jiffy.

No one will ever know, thought Horrid Henry.

Does Henry's plan to trap Father Christmas work? Find out in **'Horrid Henry's Ambush'** in **Horrid Henry's Christmas Cracker.**

Christmas Crossword

Answer the questions based on the pictures from *Horrid Henry's Ambush*, and fill in the crossword.

CLUES

Across

3. Henry is waiting for ___ ___ ___ ___ ___ ___ CHRISTMAS.

4. One of the presents is a SKIPPING ___ ___ ___ ___.

5. How many books are there in the picture of Henry's nightmare presents?

Down

1. Henry is in bed holding his GOO-___ ___ ___ ___ ___ ___ ___.

2. What is crashing onto the floor?

3. How many red baubles are there in the picture?

Clever Clare's Christmas Quiz

1. **Which fruit did people used to hang on their Christmas trees?**

   (a) Bananas
   (b) Gooseberries
   (c) Apples

2. **What does Henry want to put at the top of the Christmas tree?**

   (a) A fairy
   (b) Terminator Gladiator
   (c) Mr Kill

4. **When Christmas lunch at Horrid Henry's house turns into a disaster, what do the family end up eating instead?**

   (a) Sweet Tweet
   (b) Pizza
   (c) Pickled onion crisps

3. **Horrid Henry's parents cook a turkey for Christmas lunch, but what did people eat to celebrate Christmas in medieval England?**

   (a) Peacocks
   (b) Rats
   (c) Burgers

5. What is traditionally hidden in a Christmas pudding?

(a) A silver coin
(b) A gold gizmo
(c) A sprout

6. When Horrid Henry is given sprouts for dinner, where does he hide them?

(a) Under his plate
(b) In his pockets
(c) In a drawer

7. What are you traditionally supposed to do on Twelfth Night, the last day of Christmas?

(a) Go back to school
(b) Take down the Christmas decorations
(c) Finish all the chocolates

8. Why does Horrid Henry try and trap Father Christmas?

(a) To thank him for all the lovely presents.
(b) To give him a present in return
(c) To make sure he gets the presents he want

Turn to page 74 to see how many you scored . . .

6-8
Congratulations! You're a shining Christmas star, and as clever as Clare.

4-5
Well done! A sparkling Christmas score. But you'll have to try again to match Clever Clare's top marks.

1-3
What a pudding head! Next time, sneak a peek and copy Clever Clare's answers.

Spooky Paper Chain

Cut-out your own spooky paper chain to decorate the Christmas tree.

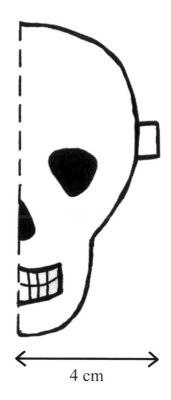

4 cm

You will need

A sheet of white A4 paper

Sticky tape

Scissors

Pencil and black crayon or felt tip pen

What to do

1. Fold the paper in half lengthways and cut it into 2 long strips. Tape the two strips together to make one longer strip.

2. Fold the strip of paper into short sections 4 cm wide.

3. Place the paper so that the top section has the folded edge on the left and the cut edge on the right.

4. Draw the outline of half a skull on the top section, making sure that all the lines run right to the edges of the section. You can use the template above if you like.

5. Cut carefully around the outline of your skull. Do not cut along the folds.

6. Unfold the paper strip to reveal a chain of skulls.

7. Colour in some scary black eyes, a hollow nose and a grinning mouth on each skull and hang the chain on your Christmas tree.

72

Answers

Page 11

There are 6 spooks hidden in the Annual.

Page 16

Nightmare New Year Quiz

1. (a)   5. (b)
2. (b)   6. (a)
3. (c)   7. (c)
4. (a)   8. (a)

Page 25

Pirate Party Time

PIRATE BLOOD BOIL BOB

Page 30

Scruffs Pet Show Puzzle

1 = F   5 = B
2 = A   6 = E
3 = C   7 = G
4 = D

Page 32

Comical Creatures Criss-cross

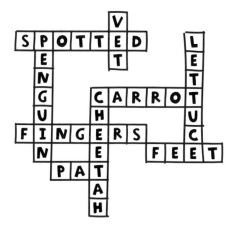

Page 33

Comical Creatures
Missing Words

1. PAT   6. LETTUCE
2. CARROT   7. SPOTTED
3. PENGUIN   8. CHEETAH
4. FEET   9. VET
5. FINGERS

Page 35

Poltergeist Puzzle

Page 37

Spot the Spooky Easter Bunny
There are 5 spooky Easter bunnies.

Page 38

Win Your Weight in Chocolate Competition

1. B   4. E   7. G
2. C   5. H   8. F
3. D   6. A

Page 43

Summer Sudoku

1	4	6	5	3	2
5	2	3	4	1	6
4	3	5	6	2	1
6	1	2	3	4	5
2	5	4	1	6	3
3	6	1	2	5	4

Page 44

The Purple Hand Gang Mystery
1.Suspects and Motives

1. Perfect Peter = MOTIVE **F**
2. Mum = MOTIVE **D**
3. Greedy Graham = MOTIVE **B**
4. Aerobic Al = MOTIVE **A**
5. Moody Margaret = MOTIVE **C**
6. Rude Ralph = MOTIVE **E**

74

2. The Clues

TOP THREE SUSPECTS	HOW LONG?	DOING WHAT?
1 Moody Margaret	30 minutes	Playing pirates
2 Rude Ralph	10 minutes	Hiding in the Fort
3 Perfect Peter	45 minutes	Helping Dad

3. The Code Letter

GOTCHA

DOWN WITH BOYS

Final answer: *Moody Margaret*

Page 47

My holiday camping with Mum and Dad was blecch. My teacher is stinky

Page 48

Match the Badge

1. 6   5. 7
2. 1   6. 8
3. 4   7. 3
4. 2   8. 5

Page 50

Chase the Chocolate Maze

Start ↓

Page 51

Greasy Greta's Sneaky Snacks

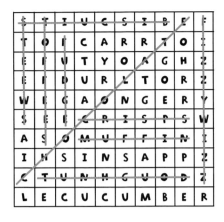

The hidden words are:
CARROT
YOGHURT
ORANGE

Page 54

Halloween Criss-cross

```
                    S
              F     W
        C O S T U M E S
            C   N   E   S
        P A R T Y   T R I C K
            O       S   D
        W E B           E
            E   M   S C A R Y
          T R E A T
        S     S
        P U M P K I N
      B O O K       I
      A   O         G
      T   K         H
                W I T C H
```

Page 61

Weird Wordsearch

T	Z	Y	V	E	S	J	R	C	G	J
H	S	B	M	P	R	E	Q	C	N	W
P	Y	I	O	M	I	J	A	O	O	F
I	V	O	E	S	U	G	W	O	T	H
L	K	F	N	G	Z	M	I	H	E	T
L	B	O	Z	B	R	W	M	O	L	C
W	M	Q	P	Q	S	E	K	S	E	L
M	N	X	H	U	M	Y	T	T	K	M
G	K	E	X	U	L	B	H	L	S	G
N	E	I	L	A	X	X	I	U	Q	K
P	H	A	N	T	O	M	Y	E	M	R

Page 63

Nightmare Maze

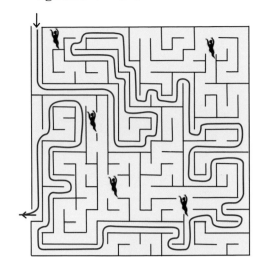

Page 69

Christmas Crossword

```
                  ¹S       ²T
  ³F A T H E R        R
    I         O        E
    V       ⁴R O P E   E
    E         T
              E
         ⁵T H R E E
```

Page 70

Clever Clare's Christmas Quiz

1. (c)   5. (a)
2. (b)   6. (c)
3. (a)   7. (b)
4. (b)   8. (c)

You can read these other *Horrid Henry* titles, stories available as audio editions, read by Miranda Richardson

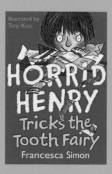

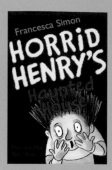

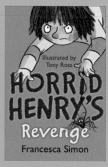
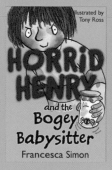

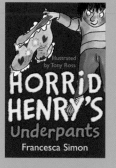

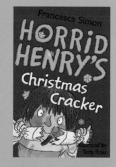
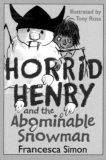

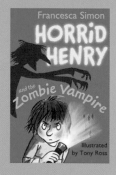

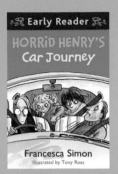    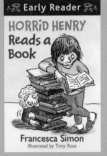 

  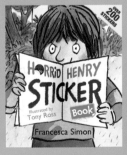 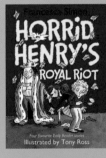 

 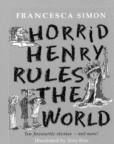  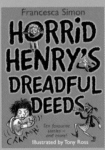 

 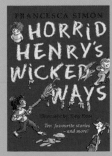  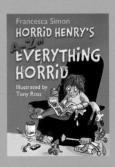